The Lighter Side of...

CRICKET

SeTo
PUBLISHING

THE LIGHTER SIDE OF CRICKET

ISBN 0 908697 34 1
© Copyright SeTo Publishing Ltd 1989

SeTo Publishing Ltd
PO Box 4028
Auckland 1
New Zealand

Printed in Hong Kong through Colorcraft

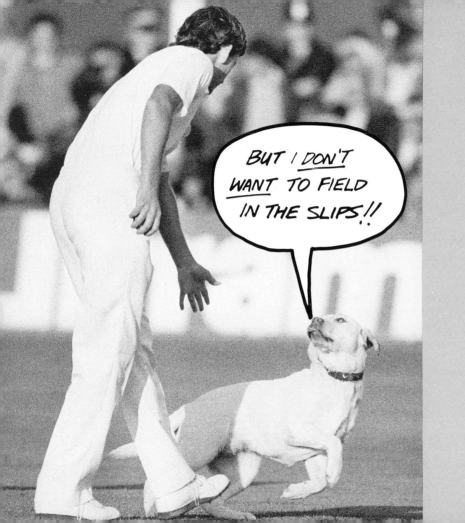

ATCO
ATCO
PLAYERS WIVES
WHERE'S YOURS, IAN?
THAT REMINDS ME GATS, SPEAKING TO YOURS YET?

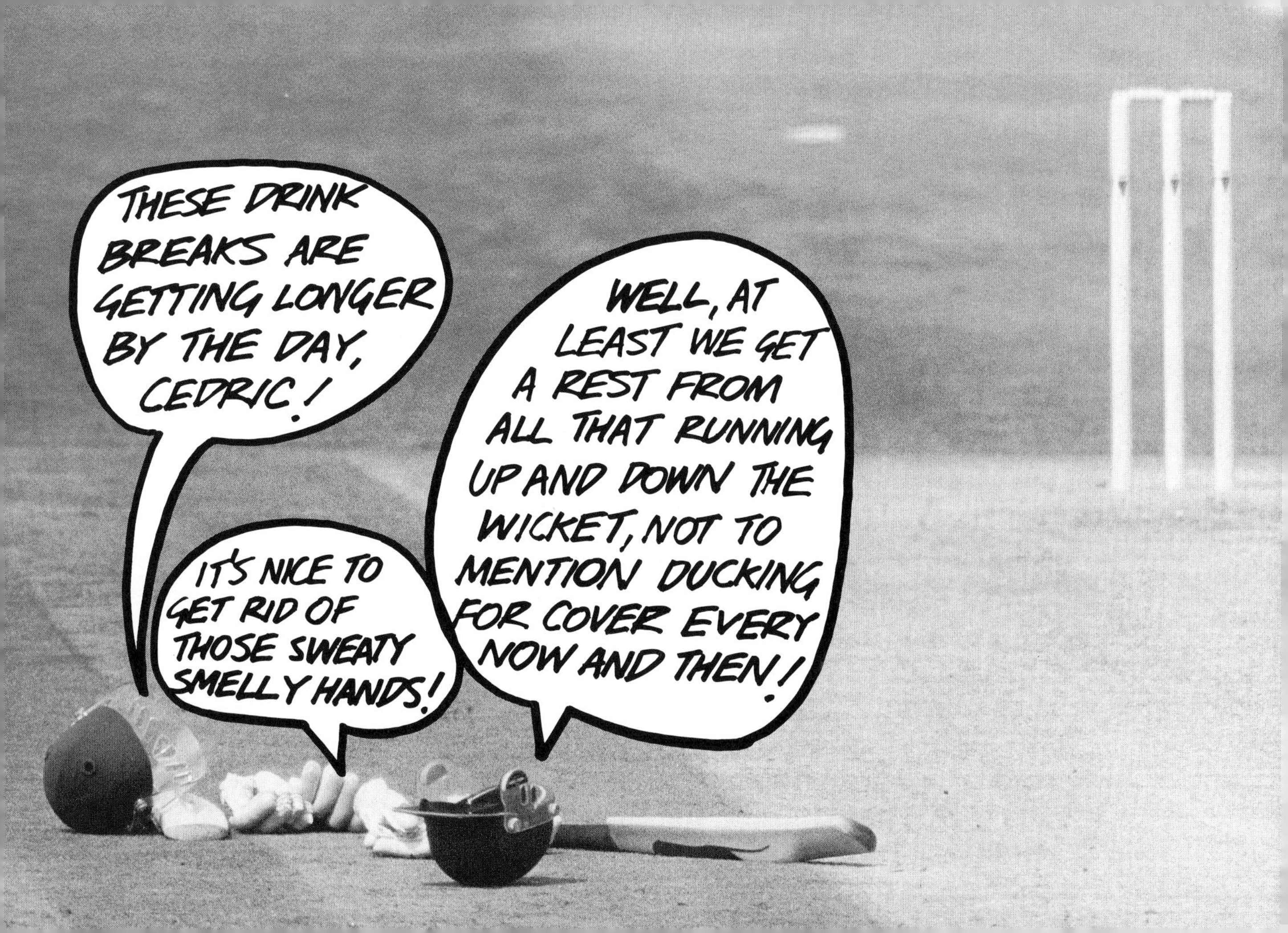
THESE DRINK BREAKS ARE GETTING LONGER BY THE DAY, CEDRIC!
IT'S NICE TO GET RID OF THOSE SWEATY SMELLY HANDS!
WELL, AT LEAST WE GET A REST FROM ALL THAT RUNNING UP AND DOWN THE WICKET, NOT TO MENTION DUCKING FOR COVER EVERY NOW AND THEN!